Peace Be Unto You
Individual Workbook

David T. Morgan, PhD

Published by David T. Morgan, PhD Inc
Vancouver, Washington

Contents

Acknowledgments

This book was more difficult to write than others, inasmuch as the format was different and it was my first attempt at a workbook-style text. I relied heavily on the feedback of others, to whom I am very grateful. As always, I'm thankful to my parents, siblings and their spouses. They are a constant source of inspiration to do better and be better. Several friends were influential in providing feedback and preparing the manuscript for publication, including Deena Morgan, Sharyle Karren, and Janet Peterson. I'm thankful for their selfless service and helpful comments. I'm very grateful to my editor, Bonnie Brien, who continues to provide generous and crucial assistance to help me hone my writing skills. She is a great blessing to me.

I'm so thankful for my children, their spouses and my grandchildren. The greatest happiness in life comes from close relationships; they have been my greatest happiness. Lastly, I'm incredibly grateful for the ongoing, selfless and patient support from my beautiful wife, Kristyn. She is everything to me. Without her, my life would be less in every way. She makes every day better and I feel like the luckiest man in the world.

Note from the Author

Many of you reading this book will have already read *Peace Be Unto You: Anxiety Management Using Gospel Principles*. In writing that book, I tried to strike a balance between doctrinal explanations and practical solutions. Yet even then, I realized that some may want additional tools to manage anxiety in their lives. Elder Dieter F. Uchtdorf taught that "spiritual light rarely comes to those who merely sit in darkness waiting for someone to flip a switch. It takes an act of faith to open our eyes to the Light of Christ."[1] The "act of faith" that Elder Uchtdorf refers to can be different for everyone but involves intentional behavior on our part. This text is designed to help readers take the next step in anxiety management. The workbook follows the original book chapter for chapter, providing additional explanation and specific questions for you to ponder and act upon. Each chapter begins with a brief summary of the corresponding chapter in *Peace Be Unto You*, exercises that are specific to the concepts and suggestions discussed in the chapter, and a review of the practical suggestions for change for that chapter. The workbook is not designed as a stand-alone volume, but as a companion text to *Peace Be Unto You*. You will find references to the original text throughout this workbook.

Remember that change involves intentional action. The more you engage in the exercises, the more change you are likely to experience. In this workbook you'll be invited to give deep and thoughtful consideration to your beliefs, self-perceptions, and fears. You'll be asked to do things that you might find somewhat anxiety-provoking at first. Yet through this process you will develop greater insight, greater strength, and

---

[1] Dieter F. Uchtdorf, "The Hope of God's Light," *Ensign*, May 2013, 75.

greater faith to manage feelings of fear and anxiety. Some may find they are quickly able to do the outlined activities and make fast progress. Others may find that the process is slow and does not yield much fruit at the outset. Don't worry about your pace; just keep moving forward. Life is a marathon, not a sprint, and we are not asked to do any more than we can at the moment (see Mosiah 4:27). Learning to manage anxiety can be a long, drawn-out process but has very valuable outcomes. Quite frankly, the harder and longer you work at it, the greater the reward. Please seek competent medical advice as necessary. I have learned that most good things in life come from hard and challenging work. We should never fear the difficult tasks; they are simply precursors to some of our greatest blessings. God bless you as you work out your salvation, learning to be more like Him by changing your lives a step at a time.

-David Morgan

In the paperback format of this workbook, spaces are provided for your responses to various questions. Even then, you may wish to use a notebook or journal to record longer responses.

Anxiety Is A Part of Life

Peace Be Unto You Chapter One Summary

Anxiety, like so many other issues, is a natural part of life. Our loving Father in Heaven does not prevent difficulties as He knows we can grow from them. Learning how to cope with our challenges is a major component of our mortal experience. Even though dealing with anxiety may prove very difficult for some, the act of working towards greater faith and peace will bless all who do this.

Exercises

Chapter One of *Peace Be Unto You* relates the story regarding Jesus calming the tempest (see Matthew 8, Luke 8, and Mark 4). At one point the disciples accuse the Savior of not being concerned for their well-being, stating, "Carest thou not that we perish?" (Mark 4:38). Yet we know the Savior has always loved and cared for us. His love never changes. It is *our perception* of His love that changes at times. The following exercises will help you better understand the Savior's love, how it applies to you, and how this relates to anxiety and your potential for change.

Many scriptures reflect the Savior's love and concern for us. Please read and study the following verses, then ponder and answer the questions that follow:

For God so loved the world, that he gave his only begotten Son, that whosoever believeth in him should not perish, but have everlasting life (John 3:16).

What does this scripture imply about Heavenly Father's love for his children?

_____

_____

_____

_____

_____

_____

_____

How do you believe this scripture applies to you personally?

_____

_____

_____

_____

_____

_____

_____

Greater love hath no man than this, that a man lay down his life for his friends (John 15:13).

What does this scripture communicate about the Savior's love for mankind?

_____

_____

_____

_____

_____

_____

What does this scripture suggest about the Savior's individual love for you?

_____

_____

_____

_____

_____

_____

Verily, thus saith the Lord unto you whom I love, and whom I love I also chasten that their sins may be forgiven, for with the chastisement I prepare a way for their deliverance in all things out of temptation, and I have loved you (Doctrine & Covenants 95:1).

Why do you believe the Lord chastens, or corrects, His children?

_____

_____

_____

_____

_____

_____

As you have been chastened or corrected by the Lord, reflect on how this could be a manifestation of His love towards you.

_____

_____

_____

_____

_____

Sometimes it is easy to think our Savior has forgotten us, especially if we feel a lack of closeness to Him. Take some time to consider your current relationship with the Savior. Briefly describe it here:

_____

_____

_____

_____

_____

_____

In what ways do you believe your relationship with the Savior could improve?

_____

_____

_____

_____

_____

_____

Reflecting on the things you wrote for the previous question, what are some things you can do in order to improve your relationship with the Savior?

_____

_____

_____

_____

_____

_____

_____

Read the account of the Savior and His disciples on the boat in Mark 4:36-41. Reflect on the reaction of Jesus Christ versus the reactions of His disciples as the storm increased. The following questions can help you analyze anxious situations and determine coping strategies. Let's examine the experience on the boat with these questions:

What was the event or circumstance? *The disciples were in a powerful, potentially deadly storm.*

Why did they have anxiety about this situation? *They thought they were going to die.*

As they tried to control the circumstance, were they successful? Why or why not? *They tried to manage the ship during the storm but were not successful. They needed additional help and figured they would drown.*

What counsel did the Savior give to them? *He encouraged them to have greater faith and then calmed the tempest.*

Now think of a recent time in your life where you experienced anxiety about an event or circumstance. Answer the following questions:

What was the event or circumstance?

_____

_____

_____

_____

_____

Why did you have anxiety about this situation?

_____

_____

_____

_____

_____

_____

_____

If you tried to control the circumstance, did you find yourself successful? Why or why not?

_____

_____

_____

_____

_____

_____

_____

Regarding this situation, what counsel do you believe the Savior would give to you?

_____

_____

_____

_____

_____

_____

Practical Suggestions

1) Try to view anxiety as a stepping-stone for growth as opposed to an impediment in your path.

In what ways can anxiety help you grow stronger?

_____

_____

_____

_____

_____

_____

2) Focus on changing your internal perspective instead of trying to change your circumstances.

What are some steps you can take to change the way you think about anxiety?

_____

_____

_____

_____

_____

You Are in Control

Peace Be Unto You Chapter Two Summary

The cognitive model is a psychological theory that explains how our emotions are a byproduct of our thoughts. Thus, anxiety can be increased or reduced by the way we think about things. Sometimes we have long-standing thought patterns that seem so routine they appear to be permanent. However, all patterns of thought can be changed through consistent practice. Initial attempts to change our thinking will often lead to failure, but learning to react to failure with humility and faith will increase overall chances for success.

Exercises

In learning to manage anxiety, it is critical to understand the connection between our thoughts and our emotions. In almost every case, thoughts come before emotions. We must learn to identify the thoughts that precede anxiety before we can effectively change them. Use the following example to practice identifying the thoughts associated with the resulting emotions.

Jane wakes up and looks out the window. Thick storm clouds have gathered, and it looks like it is going to rain. Jane has a different emotional experience based on how she thinks about the impending storm. Here are some different scenarios that can help provide context. (The first scenario contains a pattern of how to complete the exercise.)

Scenario one: Suppose Jane loves the rain, as it reminds her of summers on the farm with her grandparents. She sees the impending rain and feels very content. What are the thoughts that lead to her contentment?

Jane's thoughts are: "I love the rain! It reminds me of good times. When I hear the rain hitting the pavement, I remember Grandma and Grandpa and how much they loved me."

Scenario two: Suppose Jane is a farmer and her crops are dying due to a drought. She sees the impending rain and feels very excited. What are the thoughts that lead to her excitement?

Jane's thoughts are: _____

_____

_____

_____

_____

Scenario three: Suppose Jane is the mother of a bride who has an outdoor wedding scheduled for that day. She sees the impending rain and feels very upset. What are the thoughts that lead to her being upset?

Jane's thoughts are: _____

_____

_____

_____

_____

Scenario four: Suppose Jane has invested her life savings to promote an outdoor event that, if unsuccessful, will leave her in financial ruin. She sees the impending rain and feels very worried. What are the thoughts that lead to her worry?

Jane's thoughts are: _____

_____

_____

_____

_____

The account of Elisha and his servant in 2 Kings 6:8-17 shows how thoughts impact emotions. Both Elisha and the servant awoke to find themselves completely surrounded by a hostile army. Please read the account in 2 Kings, then answer the following questions:

How do you think Elisha felt when he first saw the armies?

_____

_____

What do you think Elisha was thinking that led to that emotion?

_____

_____

_____

How do you think the servant felt when he first saw the armies?

_____

_____

What do you think the servant was thinking that led to that emotion?

_____

_____

_____

How do you think the servant felt after he saw the heavenly guard surrounding Elisha?

_____

_____

What do you think the servant was thinking that led to that emotion?

_____

_____

_____

_____

Notice how the servant's feelings changed dramatically once he had a different perception of the situation. As we change the way we think about things, we change the way we feel about things.

On a scale of one to five, where one is "strongly disagree" and five is "strongly agree," rate yourself on the following statements:

Strongly disagree ————> Strongly agree

I believe I can become less anxious.

1   2   3   4   5

The Atonement of Jesus Christ can help me overcome anxiety.

1   2   3   4   5

If I do my part, the Lord will bless me with additional strength to overcome challenges.

1   2   3   4   5

God can help me change patterns of behavior that have been present my entire life.

1   2   3   4   5

Review your ratings to the previous statements. What do they imply about your confidence in your ability to change?

_____

_____

_____

_____

_____

Study and ponder the following scriptures, then answer the accompanying questions.

But Jesus beheld them, and said unto them, with men this is impossible; but with God all things are possible (Matthew 19:26).

Yea, for this cause I have said: Stop, and stand still until I command thee, and I will provide means whereby thou mayest accomplish the thing which I have commanded thee (Doctrine and Covenants 5:34).

But if thou canst do any thing, have compassion on us, and help us. Jesus said unto him, if thou canst believe, all things are possible to him that believeth. And straightway the father of the child cried out, and said with tears, Lord, I believe; help thou mine unbelief (Mark 9:22-24).

What do these scriptures teach regarding God's ability and willingness to help you overcome personal trials?

_____

_____

_____

_____

_____

_____

_____

In what ways do these scriptural truths apply to you?

_____

_____

_____

_____

_____

_____

_____

What specific efforts do you need to make in order to obtain God's help to manage anxiety?

_____

_____

_____

_____

_____

_____

_____

Practical Suggestions

1) Understand that feelings are a product of the way we think. As we change our thinking, we can change the way we feel.

Think of a specific example of how your thoughts affected your feelings in a certain situation. Write about this experience.

_____

_____

_____

_____

_____

2) Believe that you can change the way you think, through a combination of your own efforts and the help provided from your Heavenly Father.

Why is God's help necessary to manage any personal challenge, including anxiety?

_____

_____

_____

_____

Developing Personal Power Through the Atonement of Jesus Christ

Peace Be Unto You Chapter Three Summary

The Atonement of Jesus Christ is the mechanism of change for all improvement in life. Not only does it help us repent from sin, it also helps us change our natures to become more like our Father in Heaven. Satan has forever fought against the Savior's Atonement. His current efforts include convincing us that some of our personal flaws are beyond change, and therefore the Atonement of Jesus Christ cannot work for us. Believing that 1) we can change *any* negative personal characteristic and 2) reliance on the Savior is critical to such change is an essential foundation in anxiety management.

Exercises

Some people have dealt with anxiety issues for so long they have begun to believe they cannot change. Despite ongoing efforts, they continue to experience anxiety symptoms and therefore conclude their symptoms are permanent. This conclusion then leads to the most damaging behavior of all; *they stop trying to change.* As we better understand the purpose of trials and weakness in our lives, we learn how constant efforts to change our flaws are not just about the eventual outcome but also about how we can grow through the process.

The Book of Mormon story of the Jaredites traveling to the promised land has interesting parallels regarding how challenges can help us rely on God. This account is found in Ether chapters one through six. First, read these chapters. Second, review the following statements and answer the questions.

The Lord commanded the brother of Jared to travel to the promised land. He promised to lead them in their journey. When Jared arrived at the ocean, he realized he need to cross the sea to get to his destination. He probably had no idea when they commenced in their journey that there would be such a significant obstacle in their path. *Why would the Lord command them to travel to a location they could not get to using their own efforts alone?*

_____

_____

_____

_____

_____

The Lord commanded the brother of Jared to build barges that would preserve them as they crossed the ocean. However, when sealed tight, the barges were pitch black inside and had no external ventilation. This led the brother of Jared to ask the Lord what to do next. *Why didn't the Lord just include air and light solutions with the initial instructions for building the barge?*

_____

_____

_____

_____

_____

The Lord told the brother of Jared that "mountain waves" would smash against the barges and that there was no way they could accomplish the journey without the Lord's protection. *If the Lord's goal was for them to arrive at the promised land, why make them endure a year-long dangerous sea voyage? Why not just magically teleport them all to the promised land?*

_____

_____

_____

_____

_____

When the brother of Jared's people finally reached ground in the promised land, the scriptures record they wept for joy and recognized the extreme mercies the Lord had extended them during their journey. *How do you think the lengthy, treacherous nature of the journey increased their eventual humility and gratitude?*

_____

_____

_____

_____

_____

Let's extend this analogy to your personal efforts to manage anxiety. Use the following comparisons as you think about the Jaredite journey from a different perspective, then answer the related questions.

People of the brother of Jared = you in your mortal journey
Promised land = successful anxiety management
Ocean to cross = the ongoing efforts you make to learn anxiety management skills
Barges = the tools you use to manage anxiety

Like the Jaredites' travel to the promised land, the Lord has asked you to make a journey to manage anxiety symptoms. However, you can't get there with your own efforts alone. *Why would He ask you to do something that He knows you can't do by yourself?*

_____

_____

_____

_____

_____

Like the barges, the Lord has provided you with tools to manage anxiety (scriptures, prayer, professionals, medication, etc.), but they don't always work exactly as we'd like them to. *Why doesn't the Lord just give you the perfect tool from the beginning? Why does He want you, like the brother of Jared, to come to Him in prayer seeking additional direction?*

_____

_____

_____

_____

_____

_____

Like the ocean crossing, your efforts to manage anxiety symptoms will likely take an extended period of time. Your journey will be filled with times of darkness and danger. *If the Lord intends you to ultimately manage anxiety and therefore become more like Him, why not just magically erase your symptoms in an instant with His mighty power? Why make you go through such a long and difficult experience?*

Like the arrival at the promised land, if you trust in the Lord and keep His commandments, you will eventually be able to successfully manage anxiety symptoms. *How will your gratitude for Father in Heaven be impacted by the length of time it takes to reach your destination? For example, if you relied on the Lord and diligently sought his counsel for twenty years before achieving relief, how might your gratitude change if the whole experience only took a week?*

Remember, while successful anxiety management may be the ultimate goal, the journey you take to get there will likely bring you much closer to God and help you refine your character. In many ways, the journey itself is the reward.

Change is always possible through the Atonement of Jesus Christ. If we believe we are beyond change then we have effectively limited or eliminated His atoning power for ourselves, as people do not typically strive for something they believe they cannot obtain.

Study and ponder the following scriptures, then answer the accompanying questions. These scriptures specifically refer to repentance, which we often associate exclusively with forgiveness of sin. Try to think of repentance in more global terms, which is how we change from our current state to becoming more like God. This will help you understand how the Savior's Atonement can help you manage anxiety.

Come now, and let us reason together, saith the Lord: though your sins be as scarlet, they shall be as white as snow; though they be red like crimson, they shall be as wool (Isaiah 1:18).

O ye house of Israel whom I have spared, how oft will I gather you as a hen gathereth her chickens under her wings, if ye will repent and return unto me with full purpose of heart (3 Nephi 10:6).

Yea, and as often as my people repent will I forgive them their trespasses against me (Mosiah 26:30).

How will learning to manage anxiety help you become more like your Father in Heaven?

_____

_____

_____

_____

_____

_____

_____

_____

What do these scriptures teach about the Savior's willingness to help us change?

_____

_____

_____

_____

_____

_____

Why does the Savior want to help you, specifically and individually, to learn to manage anxiety?

_____

_____

_____

_____

_____

_____

_____

_____

_____

_____

Practical Suggestions

1) Increase your understanding of the Atonement of Jesus Christ through study and prayer.

What can you do on a daily basis to understand how the Savior's Atonement applies specifically to you?

_____

_____

_____

_____

2) Accept the fact that you will never be given a challenge you cannot eventually conquer when you combine your efforts with the power of God.

In what ways can the Lord help you in your efforts to manage anxiety?

_____

_____

_____

_____

Jacob: An Anxiety Case Study

Peace Be Unto You Chapter Four Summary

Jacob the prophet was the son of Lehi and Sariah and the brother of Nephi. He never knew the comforts of Jerusalem and was raised in a tumultuous and difficult time. In his few Book of Mormon writings, he refers to himself as "anxious" many times. Yet later writings show evidence that he seems to have managed his anxiety to a degree, replacing fear with certainty and power. An analysis of his record reveals keys we can use to develop greater faith and reduce anxiety.

Exercises

The exercises in this chapter will focus on the five principles derived from Jacob's writings. These principles are covered at length in *Peace Be Unto You*. As you complete the exercises, you can develop greater spiritual strength to face challenges with faith and confidence.

Principle #1: Be appropriately accountable

We are responsible for our own lives. Too often we focus our energy on trying to change others instead of trying to change ourselves. Trying to force change in others is wasted energy and almost always results in frustration.

Focus on changing yourself first and then seek to help others, relying on the Lord's help (see Jacob 1:19).

Read and ponder the following scriptures, then answer the related questions.

Be not deceived; God is not mocked: for whatsoever a man soweth, that shall he also reap (Galatians 6:7).

And now a commandment I give unto you—if you will be delivered you shall set in order your own house, for there are many things that are not right in your house (Doctrine and Covenants 93:43).

Why are we asked to get our own lives in order before anything else?

_____

_____

_____

_____

_____

_____

How does focusing our efforts to follow the Savior put us in a better position to help others?

_____

_____

_____

_____

_____

_____

_____

Do you feel like you have to manage the lives of others? If so, what can you do to shift greater focus to your own life?

_____

_____

_____

_____

_____

_____

Some people find it difficult to work on their own mental and emotional issues. How can you increase personal accountability to focus on making changes in your own life?

_____

_____

_____

_____

_____

_____

_____

Principle #2: Do difficult things

Anxiety is typically fueled by fear of the unknown. Often times, anxiety symptoms persist for a long time because we avoid doing what we are afraid of, thus having no opportunity to dispel fear through action. In almost every case, when we act in faith to confront our fears, we find our fears were overrated and the outcome was not as bad as we had supposed (see Jacob 2:10).

Read and ponder the following scriptures, then answer the related questions:

I can do all things through Christ which strengtheneth me (Philippians 4:13).

And it came to pass that I, Nephi, said unto my father: I will go and do the things which the Lord hath commanded, for I know that the Lord giveth no commandments unto the children of men, save he shall prepare a way for them that they may accomplish the thing which he commandeth them (1 Nephi 3:7).

Why does the Lord require us to do things that are difficult or fearful?

_____

_____

_____

_____

_____

How does understanding the doctrine in these scriptures help us develop greater faith to face personal challenges?

_____

_____

_____

_____

_____

Consider a difficult task you tend to avoid. What can you do to develop greater faith to complete this task?

_____

_____

_____

_____

_____

_____

Consider something important to accomplish but that you are afraid to do. The scriptures testify you can receive heavenly strength to do the things you fear. Why do you think the Lord will help you overcome your fear of doing this thing?

_____

_____

_____

_____

_____

_____

Principle #3: Accept your weakness

Anxiety and fear are very common conditions, yet so many people feel it is unacceptable to have such feelings. The Lord gives us weakness so we can learn to be stronger. Learning to accept our shortcomings, while still striving to overcome them, can help reduce unnecessary anxiety and help focus our emotional strength on becoming more like the Savior (see Jacob 4:6-7).

Read and ponder the following scriptures, then answer the related questions:

And if men come unto me I will show unto them their weakness. I give unto men weakness that they may be humble; and my grace is sufficient for all men that humble themselves before me; for if they humble themselves before me, and have faith in me, then will I make weak things become strong unto them (Ether 12:27).

And inasmuch as they were humble they might be made strong, and blessed from on high, and receive knowledge from time to time (Doctrine and Covenants 1:28).

Why is weakness an important precursor to developing humility?

_____

_____

_____

_____

_____

Based on the doctrine in these scriptures, what is the relationship between humility and strength?

_____

_____

_____

_____

_____

_____

What can you do to develop greater humility regarding anxiety symptoms?

_____

_____

_____

_____

_____

_____

What steps can you take to exercise greater faith in the Savior?

_____

_____

_____

_____

_____

_____

_____

Principle #4: Don't reject counsel

Our Father in Heaven is highly invested in helping us learn to increase our faith and decrease anxiety. He will provide us with opportunities to act and thus grow in spiritual power. However, His ways are often mysterious and do not appear to make much sense at first. We must learn to accept His counsel, from His mouth or the mouth of His servants, and act without doubt or complaint (see Jacob 4:10).

Read and ponder the following scriptures, then answer the related questions.

Trust in the Lord with all thine heart; and lean not unto thine own understanding. In all thy ways acknowledge him, and he shall direct thy paths (Proverbs 3:5-6).

For my thoughts are not your thoughts, neither are your ways my ways, saith the Lord. For as the heavens are higher than the earth, so are my ways higher than your ways, and my thoughts than your thoughts (Isaiah 55:8-9).

How can receiving heavenly counsel without doubting help increase our faith in God?

_____

_____

_____

_____

_____

_____

As we increase our understanding of our Heavenly Father's love for us, how will this help us accept His direction without complaint?

_____

_____

_____

_____

_____

It takes an act of faith to follow spiritual direction, especially when the outcome is uncertain. How can following such direction increase our faith?

_____

_____

_____

_____

_____

_____

_____

Consider a spiritual prompting you have received but have been reluctant to act upon. What can you do to develop greater strength to follow through with the Lord's direction?

_____

_____

_____

_____

_____

_____

_____

Principle #5: Maintain spiritual nourishment

The Spirit of the Lord inspires feelings of confidence, faith and self-assurance. These emotions are the opposite of the fear, trepidation and doubt that are inspired by anxiety. Although spiritual methods alone may not completely eradicate anxiety symptoms, the presence of the Holy Ghost in our lives will surely help to increase faith and decrease fear. Feeding our spirits is critical in learning to manage anxiety (see Jacob 6:5).

Read and ponder the following scriptures, then answer the related questions.

Thy word is a lamp unto my feet, and a light unto my path (Psalm 119:105).

Therefore ye must always pray unto the Father in my name; and whatsoever ye shall ask the Father in my name, which is right, believing that ye shall receive, behold it shall be given unto you (3 Nephi 18:19-20).

How can daily prayer and scripture study help increase faith and decrease fear?

_____

_____

_____

_____

_____

_____

Why is daily spiritual nourishment critical in our personal and spiritual development?

_____

_____

_____

_____

_____

_____

What can you do to increase the presence of the Holy Ghost in your life?

_____

_____

_____

_____

_____

_____

Consider a time when you felt the presence of the Holy Ghost very strongly. Describe the feelings you had. Then consider a time when you were highly anxious and describe those feelings. Contrast the feelings from the two different scenarios. How do they differ?

_____

_____

_____

_____

_____

_____

_____

_____

_____

Practical Suggestions

1) Follow the five outlined principles from the life of Jacob.

What can you do to intentionally implement these outlined principles in your life?

_____

_____

_____

_____

_____

2) Understand that our minds and spirits are connected, so that spiritual remedies can have influence on emotional challenges.

How can you increase your commitment to spiritual practices such as prayer, scripture study, and church and temple attendance?

_____

_____

_____

_____

_____

Using Greater Mindfulness to Manage Thoughts and Emotions

Peace Be Unto You Chapter Five Summary

Making lasting changes to our behavior is often difficult because we fail to understand the deeper causes of our actions. Our minds are often so busy that we cannot perceive the smaller experiences and sensations that ultimately combine to create anxiety reactions. As we become more mindful and aware of our internal emotional experience, we can start to see warning signs for anxiety long before such symptoms become unbearable.

Exercises

In Chapter Five of *Peace Be Unto You*, you learned about how the timing of anxiety interventions is a critical piece of symptom management. If we apply a good intervention at the wrong time, it will be less effective and may even seem inadequate for reducing anxiety. Learning which situations and circumstances tend to increase anxiety will help you time your interventions for maximum effect.

Anxiety journaling

In order to increase awareness of our experiences and be able to find places to intervene, it is helpful to have points of reference. Documenting your emotions and the experiences that happen prior to your emotions is a very good way to collect such data. The following exercise will help you assemble such information.

For the next seven days, keep an "anxiety journal." During waking hours, *once an hour*, note the following in your journal:

1. Create a rating of anxiety symptoms on a scale of one to ten, where one is no anxiety and ten is maximum anxiety.

2. Write a brief description of what happened during the hour, including any major events (e.g. "I worked for one hour"; "kids were fighting"; "boss yelled at me"; "I took a nap"; etc.)

A sample journal entry might look something like this:

Monday
10:00 a.m.
Anxiety rating: 2 of 10
What happened: kids were at school and I was able to exercise

11:00 a.m.
Anxiety rating: 2 of 10
What happened: kids were at school and I cleaned the kitchen

12:00 p.m.
Anxiety rating: 8 of 10
What happened: the school called and said that my son fell at lunch and cut his arm; I had to go to the school to take him to the doctor

Although you can be as brief as you'd like in your hourly descriptions, the more information you can provide, the better data you will have to refer to later. After a week of keeping the journal, answer the following questions:

What types of events happened during times of low anxiety (ratings of 1-3)?

_____

_____

_____

_____

_____

What types of events happened during times of moderate anxiety (ratings of 4-7)?

_____

_____

_____

_____

_____

_____

What types of events happened during times of high anxiety (ratings of 8-10)?

_____

_____

_____

_____

_____

_____

What patterns can you find in your journal? What similarities exist among the events associated with low anxiety? Moderate anxiety? High anxiety?

_____

_____

_____

_____

_____

_____

47

Pay special attention to the times when you recorded high anxiety. Go back in your journal and look at the hours that preceded those times. What events do you see? What types of situations happened before high anxiety symptoms? Can you find any patterns or similarities?

_____

_____

_____

_____

_____

_____

Using your anxiety journal for seven days is a good start. The longer you follow this process, the more data you will accumulate and the more insight you can potentially achieve. If you choose, continue using your anxiety journal and follow the same steps noted above on a weekly basis. Over time you might start to see patterns. You'll likely notice certain events that tend to trigger anxiety. The ultimate goal is to achieve insight into what types of situations tend to precede anxiety symptoms, so you can apply anxiety reduction strategies sooner than later.

Meditation preparation and practice

Chapter Five of *Peace Be Unto You* outlines a basic meditation process. The chapter contains specific instructions on how to do this. Consider developing a "meditation tracker", where you 1) determine how often you will practice meditation, and 2) document when you meditated and how it made you feel.

Prior to meditation, prayer and scripture study can be a helpful preparation. The following exercises will help you develop greater understanding about prayer and scripture study as they relate specifically to meditation.

Prayer can help us achieve greater peace and presence of mind. It can help us focus and pay attention to our internal thoughts and experiences. Read the following scriptures and answer the subsequent questions:

Pray always, and I will pour out my Spirit upon you, and great shall be your blessing—yea, even more than if you should obtain treasures of earth and corruptibleness to the extent thereof (D&C 19:38).

What is the relationship between prayer and having the Spirit in our lives?

_____

_____

_____

_____

_____

As you increase the Spirit in your life, what typically happens to your anxiety symptoms?

_____

_____

_____

_____

_____

_____

But behold, I say unto you that ye must pray always, and not faint; that ye must not perform any thing unto the Lord save in the first place ye shall pray unto the Father in the name of Christ, that he will consecrate thy performance unto thee, that thy performance may be for the welfare of thy soul (2 Nephi 32:9).

What does it mean to you to "pray always"?

_____

_____

_____

_____

_____

This scripture refers to the promise that Father in Heaven will consecrate our efforts for our good if we ask for His help through prayer. In what ways can Heavenly Father increase your ability to manage anxiety symptoms?

_____

_____

_____

_____

_____

And it came to pass that Moses began to fear exceedingly; and as he began to fear, he saw the bitterness of hell. Nevertheless, calling upon God, he received strength, and he commanded, saying: Depart from me, Satan, for this one God only will I worship, which is the God of glory (Moses 1:20).

What happened to Moses after he prayed, or "called upon God"?

_____

_____

_____

_____

_____

Describe a situation where you received additional spiritual strength after praying for assistance.

_____

_____

_____

_____

_____

_____

In what ways can God give you additional strength to manage anxiety symptoms?

_____

_____

_____

_____

_____

_____

Practical Suggestions

1) Begin a practice of regular meditation following the outlined principles.

Meditation can be an unfamiliar or even awkward process for some, but it can yield great blessings if practiced consistently. What can you do to ensure you have proper time and motivation to engage in meditation on a regular basis?

_____

_____

_____

_____

2) Develop an understanding of how as we increase awareness of our thoughts and experiences, we will be better able to intervene and make effective change.

How will recording, analyzing and becoming more aware of your thoughts help you better understand what causes your specific anxiety symptoms?

_____

_____

_____

_____

Using Visualization to Achieve Greater Peace

Peace Be Unto You Chapter Six Summary

Anxiety reactions often increase with the expectation of negative outcomes, whether such outcomes actually occur or not. If we expect something bad is going to happen, we tend to react with anxiety and fear far before the event even occurs. If we expect something good is going to happen, our emotions usually change to happiness and peace. Learning to develop a positive view of the future can help decrease anxiety symptoms.

Exercises

Sometimes we become very focused on potential negative outcomes. We anticipate the worst, and this tends to lead to greater fear and anxiety. However, when viewed objectively, there is usually little actual evidence to support either a positive or negative outcome. In reality, accurately predicting the future is very difficult. Yet one of the things we *can* do is to reflect on what has happened in the past and look for patterns that might help forecast future outcomes. The following scriptural example helps to illustrate this.

In the spring of 1820, Joseph Smith prayed to know which church he should join. It was his first vocal prayer. In response, he saw God the Father and Jesus Christ. Several years later, Joseph prayed again, seeking forgiveness of sins. He desired a heavenly manifestation confirming forgiveness. Joseph's personal writings record his thoughts: "I betook myself to prayer and supplication to Almighty God for forgiveness of all my sins and follies, and also for a manifestation to me, that I might know of my state and standing before him; *for I had full confidence in obtaining a divine manifestation, as I previously had one*" (Joseph Smith History 1:29, emphasis added). As you consider this account, please answer the following questions.

Joseph said he had "full confidence" he would receive a divine manifestation in response to his prayer. Why do you think he was so confident?

_____

_____

_____

_____

How can a past experience increase our confidence in having a similar experience in the future?

_____

_____

_____

_____

_____

Let's review some experiences you've had that you thought were not going to work out well but actually did. First, describe the experience. Second, detail why you thought it would not work out. Third, detail what actually happened. Here's an example from my own life, many years ago:

Experience: *I applied for pre-doctoral internships.*

What I thought would happen: *I thought I would not get accepted to any internship and thus my educational goals would be delayed.*

What actually happened: *I got accepted to an internship and finished my education according to my schedule.*

Choose two experiences from your life. These should be situations that you thought would not work out well but ultimately did. Follow the pattern as you describe the situations and your related perceptions:

Experience #1: _____

_____

What I thought would happen: _____

_____

_____

What actually happened: _____

_____

_____

Experience #2: _____

_____

What I thought would happen: _____

_____

_____

What actually happened: _____

_____

_____

In truth, you are probably able to come up with many, many more experiences similar to the ones you outlined above. There is probably much evidence in your life to suggest that things you worried about at one time eventually worked out well. This does not mean there was no difficulty and trial before the favorable outcome resulted. But most of the time, our catastrophic fears of certain future events are 1) overreactions and 2) do not happen as we anticipated.

Now let's analyze some of your current worries and fears. These should be things that you are presently concerned about and the outcome is yet uncertain. First, describe the event. Second, come up with a catastrophic *negative* outcome. Third, imagine a completely unrealistic *positive* outcome. You'll describe the likelihood of each outcome. Finally, you'll come up with a more reasonable result. I'll provide another personal example.

Current worry: *I'm afraid this book won't sell very many copies.*

Potential catastrophic outcome: *The book will sell zero copies. Not even my friends or family will read it. It will be banned from the Library of Congress and never see the light of day.*

Potential incredible outcome: *The book will sell one trillion copies. It will become the best-selling book of all time. The Library of Congress will name a wing after me.*

How likely is the catastrophic outcome? *Very unlikely.*

How likely is the incredible outcome? *Very unlikely.*

Write down a more likely outcome to this situation: *The book will sell a decent amount of copies. I won't become rich, but I'll learn from the process. There will be some who feel it is very valuable and helpful. I'll feel proud of myself for completing a personal goal.*

Now it's your turn. Choose two current experiences where you are worried about a potential outcome and answer the following questions:

Current worry #1: _____

_____

Potential catastrophic outcome: _____

_____

_____

Potential incredible outcome: _____

_____

_____

How likely is the catastrophic outcome? _____

_____

How likely is the incredible outcome? _____

_____

Write down a more likely outcome to this situation:

_____

_____

_____

Current worry #2: _____

_____

Potential catastrophic outcome: _____

_____

_____

Potential incredible outcome: _____

_____

_____

How likely is the catastrophic outcome? _____

_____

How likely is the incredible outcome? _____

_____

Write down a more likely outcome to this situation:

_____

_____

_____

Visualization preparation and practice

Chapter Six of *Peace Be Unto You* outlines a basic visualization process. The chapter contains specific instructions on how to do this. Consider developing a "visualization tracker", where you 1) determine how often you will practice visualization, and 2) document when you visualized and how it made you feel.

Prior to visualization, prayer and scripture study can be a helpful preparation. The following exercises will help you develop greater understanding of the peace your Father in Heaven can help you feel.

These things I have spoken unto you, that in me ye might have peace. In the world ye shall have tribulation: but be of good cheer; I have overcome the world (John 16:33).

What does it mean to you to have peace "in" the Savior?

_____

_____

_____

_____

_____

_____

Knowing that Jesus Christ has "overcome the world," how can this help you have greater confidence on a daily basis?

_____

_____

_____

_____

_____

_____

_____

Yea, and it came to pass that the Lord our God did visit us with assurances that he would deliver us; yea, insomuch that he did speak peace to our souls, and did grant unto us great faith, and did cause us that we should hope for our deliverance in him (Alma 58:11).

Describe a time in your past when the Lord "visited you with assurances", or otherwise gave you comfort, regarding some situation that caused anxiety.

_____

_____

_____

_____

_____

How does reflecting on that experience help increase your faith in God?

_____

_____

_____

_____

Did I not speak peace to your mind concerning the matter? What greater witness can you have than from God? (Doctrine and Covenants 6:23).

Describe the differences between your own anxious thoughts and the calming, peaceful thoughts that come through the Holy Ghost.

_____

_____

_____

_____

_____

_____

What can you do to increase the companionship of the Spirit on a daily basis?

_____

_____

_____

_____

_____

_____

My son, peace be unto thy soul; thine adversity and thine afflictions shall be but a small moment (Doctrine and Covenants 121:7).

How does it make you feel when you realize that all trials and troubles will eventually end?

_____

_____

_____

_____

_____

How can increased faith in Jesus Christ help strengthen your ability to endure personal challenges?

_____

_____

_____

_____

_____

_____

Practical Suggestions

1) Begin a regular practice of visualization following the outlined principles.

Visualization can be an unfamiliar or even awkward process for some, but it can yield great blessings if practiced consistently. What can you do to ensure you have proper time and motivation to engage in visualization on a regular basis?

_____

_____

_____

_____

2) Develop an understanding of how the way we foresee future events, either positively or negatively, can have an effect on the emotions we feel in the present.

How will becoming less subjective and less negative about the future help you decrease anxiety symptoms?

_____

_____

_____

_____

_____

CHAPTER SEVEN

Changing Thought Patterns Changes Emotional Reactions

Peace Be Unto You Chapter Seven Summary

We have already established that emotions develop from the way we think about things. Accurate perception of situations leads to emotional reactions consistent with the circumstance. Inaccurate perception of situations leads to emotions that are usually inconsistent and distressing. Cognitive distortions are thought patterns that are incorrect but can be changed with awareness and effort. As we learn to change our thoughts and align them with an accurate assessment of reality, our emotional experience can be less extreme and more peaceful.

Exercises

Patterns of thought, especially those we have held for a long time, can be difficult to change. Habits of thought are similar to habits of behavior. When we do behaviors over and over, they tend to become easier and more automatic. Thinking is the same; the more we think certain thoughts (positive or negative), the more automatic they become. Changing thought patterns requires discipline and endurance. However, first we need to identify inaccurate thought patterns so we can target them for change.

Shortly after his father's death, the prophet Nephi appears to have had a small crisis of faith. His brothers, Laman and Lemuel, were plotting civil war. Nephi had become the spiritual leader of his people. It seems he felt

66

overwhelmed and inadequate for the task ahead. In 2 Nephi chapter 4, verses 15 through 35 are commonly referred to as the "psalm of Nephi." In these verses, Nephi expresses thoughts regarding his weakness but also the ways the Lord has supported him. Please read the following scriptures and answer the related questions.

Read 2 Nephi 4:17-19.

Why do you think Nephi believes he is a "wretched man"?

_____

_____

_____

_____

Based on what you might know about Nephi's life, do you think he was a wretched man? Why or why not?

_____

_____

_____

_____

_____

Read 2 Nephi 4:20-35.

What evidence do you find in these verses that Nephi is not a wretched man, but actually a stalwart child of God?

_____

_____

_____

_____

_____

Nephi's experience teaches that even prophets have bad days and negative thoughts. As he reflected on past experiences and gospel truths, he was able to change his perceptions and see himself and his situation in a clearer and more positive focus.

Cognitive distortions, or negative thinking patterns, are very common. Practically everyone uses them to one degree or another. Generally speaking, they are global and extreme. Here are a few examples:

1. Nobody likes me.
2. I can't change the way I am.
3. I have no valuable skills.

Such thoughts, when repeated over and over, can create a negative mindset. They can fuel feelings of anxiety and fear. Often such thoughts are based on limited experience but have since been blown out of proportion and scope. For example, you may have experienced past rejection, but now hold the extreme belief that "nobody likes me." A single rejection, even multiple rejections, does not support the idea that no one out there likes or accepts you. Let's look at more reasonable versions of these cognitive distortions:

1. *Nobody likes me.* Instead: Some people out there don't like me, but there are others who do.

2. *I can't change the way I am.* Instead: I struggle to change certain aspects of my personality, but I believe with new skills and continued effort I can eventually make progress.

3. *I have no valuable skills.* Instead: I'm not very good at certain things, but I do have some things to contribute.

Following the aforementioned pattern and example, write down two cognitive distortions you have. These should be negative or inaccurate beliefs about yourself.

Distortion #1: _____

_____

_____

Distortion #2: _____

_____

_____

Now write down more reasonable and accurate versions of those distortions:

Reasonable version #1: _____

_____

_____

Reasonable version #2: _____

_____

_____

Chapter Seven of *Peace Be Unto You* contains a six-step process you can use to analyze and modify cognitive distortions. As you review the example in that chapter it will help you understand and complete the following assignment. For this assignment, think about a recent event where you experienced considerable anxiety. Use the details of this event to answer the following questions. The more detail you can provide, the more information you will have to effectively assess and correct inaccurate thinking.

Describe the situation

What happened? _____

_____

_____

_____

When did the anxiety symptoms begin? _____

_____

_____

_____

Was there anything out of the ordinary that happened? If so, what?

_____

_____

_____

Describe your thoughts

What did you think about the situation? _____

_____

_____

_____

What particular thoughts increased your feelings of anxiety?

_____

_____

_____

Summarize your thoughts about this event into a one sentence statement. (This will be similar to the examples of cognitive distortions we looked at earlier in this chapter.)

_____

_____

_____

Describe your feelings

How did you feel? _____

_____

_____

How long did the feelings last? _____

_____

_____

When did the feelings stop? _____

_____

_____

How were you able to calm yourself down? _____

_____

_____

_____

Scrutinize your thinking

Refer to the one-sentence statement you developed in the "describe your thoughts" section.

What is accurate about this statement? _____

_____

_____

_____

What is inaccurate about this statement? _____

_____

_____

_____

Search for doctrine

Refer to the one-sentence statement you developed in the "describe your thoughts" section. Identify some key concepts that describe your statement (such as fear, hopelessness, weakness, etc.)

What do the scriptures teach about these key concepts?

_____

_____

_____

What have living prophets taught about these key concepts?

_____

_____

_____

Identify accurate beliefs

Refer to the one-sentence statement you developed in the "describe your thoughts" section. Now write a different version of this statement, based on accurate thinking and doctrine you've studied.

_____

_____

_____

Practical Suggestions

1) Start becoming more aware of your experiences, thoughts, and feelings using the outlined principles.

What can you do to start paying more attention to your thought patterns? What can you do to analyze and confront inaccurate thinking?

_____

_____

_____

_____

_____

2) Accept the fact that you can change your thought patterns through consistent, dutiful effort.

What particular patterns of thought would you like to change?

_____

_____

_____

_____

_____

CHAPTER EIGHT

Greater Coping Strategies Increase Anxiety Tolerance

Peace Be Unto You Chapter Eight Summary

Life is full of difficult experiences. Each day seems to bring a new challenge. But this is a critical part of our Heavenly Father's plan for our growth. If we surrender in the face of difficulty, we are simply missing out on opportunities for eternal progression. Persistence develops strength, even if we never fully conquer our challenges in this life. As we modify our thinking and develop more flexible views of our circumstances, we can find tools that will help us have greater peace and less anxiety.

Exercises

Anxiety tends to increase on the expectation of the unknown. We consider possible scenarios and develop extreme potential outcomes. Anxiety builds with each unlikely negative consequence. However, looking closely and objectively at such outcomes, we can gain greater insight. As we combine our new perception with gospel truth, anxiety symptoms can be reduced.

Chapter Eight of *Peace Be Unto You* talks about how developing new perspectives can help decrease anxiety. Read Doctrine and Covenants 122:5-9 and answer the following questions:

Despite a list of very negative potential outcomes, the Lord invited Joseph to think differently about them. What are the ways He asked Joseph to think more positively and hopefully about apparently negative situations?

_____

_____

_____

_____

_____

Why do you think changing our perspective about things will change the way we feel?

_____

_____

_____

_____

_____

_____

Analyzing our fears can help us create tools to move forward. Chapter Eight of *Peace Be Unto You* teaches a pattern for how to do this, including asking questions about why certain situations cause anxiety, what can be done about it, and what the scriptures teach about similar situations.

Let's look at a scriptural example to help model this process. Consider Nephi's experience of going to retrieve the plates of brass (see 1 Nephi 4:5-18). After two failed attempts, he went alone to Laban's house, relying on the Spirit for direction. He found Laban drunk and unconscious. The Spirit told Nephi he needed to kill Laban. Nephi reacted with fear and trepidation. Let's analyze his experience, imagining it from Nephi's perspective, using the pattern taught in Chapter Eight of *Peace Be Unto You.*

Experience: *The Spirit has commanded me to kill Laban.*

Why does this cause anxiety to me? *I've never killed anyone before. I've never even thought about doing it. It seems very wrong.*

What can I do about it? *I can pray for additional direction and strength.*

What do the scriptures teach about such situations? *We need to keep the commandments in order to be blessed of the Lord. The commandments, including all the many requirements of the Law of Moses, are contained on the brass plates. If we don't have the brass plates, we won't be able to correctly follow the law. The Lord has delivered Laban into my hands so that I can preserve my people in righteousness.*

Nephi was able to follow through with the Lord's command, notwithstanding his fears, as he addressed and resolved his concerns. We can do the same.

Create a list of three experiences that cause anxiety for you. Choose one that causes low anxiety, one that causes moderate anxiety, and one that causes high anxiety. List each experience and then answer the following questions.

Experience 1 (low anxiety): _____

_____

_____

Why does this cause anxiety to me? _____

_____

_____

What can I do about it? _____

_____

_____

What do the scriptures teach about such situations?

_____

_____

_____

Experience 2 (moderate anxiety): _____

_____

_____

Why does this cause anxiety to me? _____

_____

_____

What can I do about it? _____

_____

_____

What do the scriptures teach about such situations?

_____

_____

_____

Experience 3 (high anxiety): _____

_____

_____

Why does this cause anxiety to me? _____

_____

_____

What can I do about it? _____

_____

_____

What do the scriptures teach about such situations?

_____

_____

_____

You can repeat this process any time you encounter a situation where anxiety creates sufficient fear that you feel you cannot move forward. As you develop greater understanding and perspective, you can gain increased strength to act in faith despite your fears.

Chapter Eight of *Peace Be Unto You* also outlines the difference between unacceptable and undesirable outcomes. Sometimes we experience anxiety about possible outcomes because we have already concluded that specific results are completely unacceptable. For example, say we hope to get hired for a new job. If we believe the *only* way we'll be happy is to get that specific job. In that case, all other potential outcomes are *unacceptable* and can lead to devastating anxiety and disappointment. Yet if we believe that it is simply *undesirable* to not get that job, alternate outcomes can still be disappointing but are not so emotionally crushing.

Consider the case of Shadrach, Meshach and Abednego as recounted in Daniel chapter 3. These faithful Israelites refused to worship the king's pagan gods, even when noncompliance carried the threat of death. They were taken into custody for their refusal, brought to a fiery furnace, and threatened to be burned alive if they did not comply with the king's demands. They told the king they knew their God could save them from the flames, *but if not,* they would still be faithful to God's commands. Let's apply this to the unacceptable vs. undesirable notion.

If burning alive were completely "unacceptable" to Shadrach, Meshach and Abednego, perhaps they would have compromised their values and bowed to the king's wishes. Surely, they did not want to lose their lives. But it seems that burning alive was simply "undesirable" to the youth. They likely saw death as an undesirable outcome, but nothing so extreme that they would choose to serve other Gods to avoid it. They were willing to accept the possible fatal outcome, thus increasing their faith and peace of mind. Chapter Eight of *Peace Be Unto You* outlines some questions that can be applied to help understand unacceptable vs. undesirable outcomes. Let's apply these questions to the situation with Shadrach, Meshach and Abednego.

What is the worry? *The king has threatened to kill me.*

What do I want to happen? *I would like to be released without harm.*

Why is this potential outcome so important to me? *I don't want to be burned alive.*

Why do I feel like anything but this certain outcome will be unacceptable? *I want to keep living my life and serving the Lord.*

What will really happen if things don't work out the way I want them to? *I will lose my life, but I will go on to a great reward and be blessed for my obedience.*

If things don't go my way, what will the Lord do to continue to support me? *He will bless me, one day raise me from the dead, and eventually I will be brought back to His presence to live with Him forever.*

Most likely none of you are facing such deadly outcomes with current situations in your life, but there are many issues where we feel like certain results are unacceptable. Take some time to think of some of your most significant worries. Some examples can include outcomes related to extended family members, children, employment, education, health concerns, and so on. Consider two such worries and answer the following questions.

Worry 1:

What is the worry? _____

_____

What do I want to happen? _____

_____

_____

_____

Why is this potential outcome so important to me?

_____

_____

_____

_____

Why do I feel like anything but this certain outcome will be unacceptable?

_____

_____

_____

_____

What will really happen if things don't work out the way I want them to?

_____

_____

_____

_____

_____

If things don't go my way, what will the Lord do to continue to support me?

_____

_____

_____

_____

_____

Worry 2:

What is the worry? _____

_____

What do I want to happen? _____

_____

_____

_____

Why is this potential outcome so important to me?

_____

_____

_____

_____

Why do I feel like anything but this certain outcome will be unacceptable?

_____

_____

_____

_____

_____

What will really happen if things don't work out the way I want them to?

_____

_____

_____

_____

_____

If things don't go my way, what will the Lord do to continue to support me?

_____

_____

_____

_____

_____

One of the main promises of the Atonement of Jesus Christ is that all will work out well to those who do their best to act in faith and keep their covenants. Understanding and applying His Atonement in our lives is critical to the development of faith and peace. Study the following scriptures and answer the related questions.

For it is expedient that an atonement should be made; for according to the great plan of the Eternal God there must be an atonement made, or else all mankind must unavoidably perish; yea, all are hardened; yea, all are fallen and are lost, and must perish except it be through the atonement which it is expedient should be made (Alma 34:9).

How does understanding the essential nature of the Atonement of Jesus Christ help increase your dependence upon Him?

_____

_____

_____

_____

_____

_____

How can you increase your reliance on the Atonement of Jesus Christ?

_____

_____

_____

_____

_____

_____

And the presence of God withdrew from Moses, that his glory was not upon Moses; and Moses was left unto himself. And it came to pass that it was for the space of many hours before Moses did again receive his natural strength like unto man; and he said unto himself: Now, for this cause I know that man is nothing, which thing I never had supposed (Moses 1:9-10).

Why is it important to realize you are "nothing" compared to the glorious power of God?

_____

_____

_____

_____

_____

How can increased humility lead to greater acts of faith on your part?

_____

_____

_____

_____

_____

_____

For we labor diligently to write, to persuade our children, and also our brethren, to believe in Christ, and to be reconciled to God; for we know that it is by grace that we are saved, after all we can do (2 Nephi 25:23).

Why is it critical for us to do all we can, exercising our strongest efforts, to keep the commandments and return to Heavenly Father?

_____

_____

_____

_____

_____

How do you feel when you realize the Lord will compensate for your weakness?

_____

_____

_____

_____

_____

Practical Suggestions

1) Begin to see trials as growth opportunities.

How can anxiety symptoms help you eventually become closer to the Savior?

_____

_____

_____

_____

_____

_____

2) Understand how the Atonement of Jesus Christ means you simply have to do your best, and failures are part of the plan.

How can you utilize the Atonement of Jesus Christ in your life on a daily basis?

_____

_____

_____

_____

_____

3) Distinguish between unacceptable and undesirable outcomes.

How can developing more flexible thinking help reduce anxiety symptoms?

_____

_____

_____

_____

_____

How Increasing Feelings of Love Decreases Feelings of Anxiety

Peace Be Unto You Chapter Nine Summary

One of the primary goals of life is to change our natures from carnal and worldly to spiritual and holy. Anything that makes us different from Father in Heaven needs to be purged and replaced with celestial qualities. We have been commanded to love others as we love ourselves. Implicit in this commandment is a charge to have an appropriate and healthy love of self. As we learn to love ourselves as Heavenly Father loves us, we will develop greater confidence and less anxiety.

Exercises

As He prayed in the last supper, Jesus taught as follows: "And this is life eternal, that they might know thee the only true God, and Jesus Christ, whom thou hast sent" (John 17:3). He seems to establish a connection between eternal life, or exaltation, and coming to truly know Himself and His Father. Developing an accurate perception of our Father in Heaven and Jesus Christ is critical in understanding how much they love us. Read and study the following scriptures, then answer the related questions.

For behold, this is my work and my glory—to bring to pass the immortality and eternal life of man (Moses 1:39).

Can a woman forget her sucking child, that she should not have compassion on the son of her womb? Yea, they may forget, yet will I not forget thee. Behold, I have graven thee upon the palms of my hands; thy walls are continually before me (Isaiah 49:15-16).

Now have we not reason to rejoice? Yea, I say unto you, there never were men that had so great reason to rejoice as we, since the world began; yea, and my joy is carried away, even unto boasting in my God; for he has all power, all wisdom, and all understanding; he comprehendeth all things, and he is a merciful Being, even unto salvation, to those who will repent and believe on his name (Alma 26:35).

What do these scriptures teach about the Savior's personal love for you?

_____

_____

_____

_____

_____

_____

Based on the doctrine in these scriptures, do you believe the Savior is patient with your shortcomings? Why or why not?

_____

_____

_____

_____

_____

What type of person do you believe the Savior wants you to become in this life?

_____

_____

_____

_____

Learning to love ourselves can be a difficult task for some. We are taught many subtle lessons throughout life that contribute to our overall sense of self-concept. Some of these life lessons increase positive feelings while others create negativity. In this next exercise, please make an honest self-assessment regarding your current level of love for self.

On a scale of one to five, where one is "strongly disagree" and five is "strongly agree," rate yourself on the following statements:

Strongly disagree ————→ Strongly agree

I feel confident on a regular basis.

| 1 | 2 | 3 | 4 | 5 |

I love the type of person I am becoming.

| 1 | 2 | 3 | 4 | 5 |

I know the Savior loves me personally.

| 1 | 2 | 3 | 4 | 5 |

I am a good example to others.

| 1 | 2 | 3 | 4 | 5 |

I feel like Heavenly Father is proud of me.

| 1 | 2 | 3 | 4 | 5 |

Examine your responses. For any items where you circled a one or a two, you may need to do some work to increase your feelings of love for self. Remember, our Father in Heaven sees us to the core, complete with all our weakness and shortcomings. Yet He is the one who loves us the most. To Him, we are innately loveable and worthwhile. As we develop thought patterns that make us feel *less* loveable and *less* worthwhile, we are being influenced by the adversary's lies.

For each statement where you rated yourself a one or two, answer the following questions:

Why did I give myself such a rating?

_____

_____

_____

_____

_____

_____

Based on what I know from scripture and the words of modern prophets, how would the Lord rate me on the same statement?

_____

_____

_____

_____

_____

_____

What can I do to close the gap between my perceptions of myself and how the Lord feels about me?

_____

_____

_____

_____

_____

_____

Chapter Nine of *Peace Be Unto You* reviews a number of scriptures that discuss the Savior's love for us. We need to accurately understand His love so that we can learn to apply it to ourselves and others. For this next exercise, please read and study these scriptures from Chapter Nine and answer the associated questions.

O ye house of Israel whom I have spared, how oft will I gather you as a hen gathereth her chickens under her wings, if ye will repent and return unto me with full purpose of heart (3 Nephi 10:6).

Why do you think the Savior is so patient with those who sin?

_____

_____

_____

_____

Why will the Savior continue to seek after you, regardless of your weakness and disobedience?

_____

_____

_____

_____

_____

When Jesus had lifted up himself, and saw none but the woman, he said unto her, Woman, where are those thine accusers? hath no man condemned thee? She said, No man, Lord. And Jesus said unto her, neither do I condemn thee: go, and sin no more (John 8:10-11).

How is the Savior able to have such love for those who have sinned so greatly?

_____

_____

_____

_____

_____

_____

How can His example help you be more patient with yourself when you make poor decisions?

_____

_____

_____

_____

_____

_____

We love him, because he first loved us (1 John 4:19).

How does it make you feel to know the Savior has always loved you?

_____

_____

_____

_____

_____

_____

Does knowing the Savior has always loved you make it easier for you to love yourself? Why or why not?

_____

_____

_____

_____

_____

_____

_____

Greater love hath no man than this, that a man lay down his life for his friends (John 15:13).

Based on this scripture, describe the Savior's love for mankind.

_____

_____

_____

_____

_____

Based on this scripture, describe the Savior's individual love for you.

_____

_____

_____

_____

_____

_____

For God so loved the world, that he gave his only begotten Son, that whosoever believeth in him should not perish, but have everlasting life (John 3:16).

What does this scripture teach about God's estimation of your divine potential?

_____

_____

_____

_____

_____

_____

What can you do to love yourself more like Heavenly Father loves you?

_____

_____

_____

_____

_____

_____

Practical Suggestions

1) Prayerfully seek to understand and feel the depth of God's individual and personal love for you.

What things can you pray about on a daily basis to better feel God's love for you?

_____

_____

_____

_____

_____

_____

2) Seek to develop greater confidence in and love for yourself, using the love of God as a benchmark and model.

What can you do to achieve a better understanding of how God loves you?

_____

_____

_____

_____

_____

How to Better Understand and Help Those Who Deal with Anxiety

Peace Be Unto You Chapter Ten Summary

This chapter is unique as it is written to those who do not necessarily experience anxiety but who are trying to support those who do. Their experiences can often be as frustrating as yours, but for different reasons. Ten suggestions are offered regarding how others can provide support and encouragement as you strive to manage anxiety symptoms.

Exercises

Helping someone else change can often be as difficult as going through the change process yourself. You may have people in your life who are concerned about you. They worry about your situation and strive to help where they can. At times, their efforts can be misguided and fall flat. But almost always, their motivations are sincere. There are things you can do in order to help them help you. Chapter Ten of *Peace Be Unto You* contains ten principles that are designed to guide the assistance of those trying to provide support to you. Here are five additional suggestions that will help you better receive their support. Read and ponder each suggestion and the accompanying scriptures, then answer the associated questions.

Take responsibility for your own behavior. Don't make others feel guilty for your choices. Even though they are trying to help, your anxiety issues are chiefly your concern. Others can certainly provide assistance, but you need to be the one who takes primary accountability for your choices and emotional experience.

That every man may act in doctrine and principle pertaining to futurity, according to the moral agency which I have given unto him, that every man may be accountable for his own sins in the day of judgment (Doctrine & Covenants 101:78).

What is the relationship between having moral agency and being accountable for your own choices?

_____

_____

_____

_____

_____

_____

_____

_____

_____

And it is requisite with the justice of God that men should be judged according to their works; and if their works were good in this life, and the desires of their hearts were good, that they should also, at the last day, be restored unto that which is good (Alma 41:3).

Knowing you will be judged according to your choices, how does this influence your motivation to do your part to manage anxiety symptoms?

_____

_____

_____

_____

_____

_____

_____

_____

<u>Provide for yourself emotionally and spiritually.</u> While it is very appropriate to derive some strength and support from others, they cannot be your only source of emotional encouragement. Avoid becoming such a drain on others that they have a hard time meeting their own needs.

Pray always, that you may come off conqueror; yea, that you may conquer Satan, and that you may escape the hands of the servants of Satan that do uphold his work (Doctrine & Covenants 10:5).

How will regular, sincere prayer help you build emotional and spiritual strength?

_____

_____

_____

_____

_____

_____

_____

_____

_____

_____

But this much I can tell you, that if ye do not watch yourselves, and your thoughts, and your words, and your deeds, and observe the commandments of God, and continue in the faith of what ye have heard concerning the coming of our Lord, even unto the end of your lives, ye must perish. And now, O man, remember, and perish not (Mosiah 4:30).

What can you do to be better aware of the patterns of thoughts, words and actions that ultimately influence your emotional experience?

_____

_____

_____

_____

_____

_____

_____

Try not to complain excessively about your situation. There is nothing wrong with periodic venting. However, when we take an objective look at our lives, we typically have many more blessings than we have difficulties. Adopting an attitude of gratitude can ease your burden and inspire those who assist you.

Enter into his gates with thanksgiving, and into his courts with praise: be thankful unto him, and bless his name (Psalm 100:4).

If you were to increase feelings of gratitude for what you have, how would that affect your overall attitude?

_____

_____

_____

_____

_____

_____

_____

_____

_____

_____

And now I would that ye should be humble, and be submissive and gentle; easy to be entreated; full of patience and long-suffering; being temperate in all things; being diligent in keeping the commandments of God at all times; asking for whatsoever things ye stand in need, both spiritual and temporal; always returning thanks unto God for whatsoever things ye do receive (Alma 7:23).

How will faith in God help you be grateful for both the blessings *and* trials that come from your Father in Heaven?

_____

_____

_____

_____

_____

_____

_____

_____

Be patient when receiving assistance from others. In most cases, others are trying their best to help. Often, they have little understanding of what will actually be effective and are simply doing what they feel is right. Try to receive their support in the spirit in which it is intended. Avoid becoming bitter or angry when others don't help the way you would like them to.

He that is slow to wrath is of great understanding: but he that is hasty of spirit exalteth folly (Proverbs 14:29).

As you strive to presume good intentions behind the behavior of others, how will this help you become more Christlike?

_____

_____

_____

_____

_____

_____

_____

_____

_____

_____

For ye have need of patience, that, after ye have done the will of God, ye might receive the promise (Hebrews 10:36).

How might an increase in patience lead to a decrease in anxiety?

_____

_____

_____

_____

_____

_____

_____

_____

_____

_____

<u>Try to see things from multiple perspectives</u>. It is important to realize that people who are trying to help you with your problems have problems of their own. We are all suffering in one way or another. Striving to be compassionate with others in the midst of your own challenges is a highly Christlike characteristic. Practice it as much as you can.

Bear ye one another's burdens, and so fulfil the law of Christ (Galatians 6:2).

Consider a time when you have reached out to help someone else, even when you were suffering yourself. How did that act of service affect you?

_____

_____

_____

_____

_____

_____

_____

_____

_____

_____

_____

Thus speaketh the Lord of hosts, saying, execute true judgment, and shew mercy and compassions every man to his brother (Zechariah 7:9).

How can being compassionate and trying to understand another's situation help you better manage your own emotional struggles?

_____

_____

_____

_____

_____

_____

_____

_____

_____

_____

Practical Suggestions

1) Develop a greater understanding of the Savior's love for you and then use that as a model to love and support others.

How will you be better able to help others as you develop an increased awareness of the Savior's remarkable concern for you?

_____

_____

_____

_____

_____

2) Reflect on your own challenges and use these experiences to develop greater empathy for those around you.

How can your own trials help you better understand and help those who are suffering from similar difficulties?

_____

_____

_____

_____

_____

Confidence is Key to Change

Peace Be Unto You Chapter Eleven Summary

All personal change requires action on our part. We must act first and then the Lord will provide assistance as needed. Taking responsibility for our thoughts and emotions is critical in learning to manage anxiety symptoms. Being the first to act, and not waiting for someone else to rescue us from our circumstance, requires faith and strength. We need to work diligently to do our part and then rely on the Lord for what is lacking. Many, many scriptural evidences confirm that we will receive the Lord's help when we have done our part.

Exercises

Our Father in Heaven is very willing to bless us according to our needs and wants. However, in order to help us develop faith, He invites us to act first. As you study the scriptures, you will find many of these invitations. Please read and ponder the following scripture and then answer the ensuing questions.

Draw near unto me and I will draw near unto you; seek me diligently and ye shall find me; ask, and ye shall receive; knock, and it shall be opened unto you (Doctrine and Covenants 88:63).

What does it mean to you to "draw near unto the Lord"?

_____

_____

_____

_____

_____

_____

What is the difference between seeking the Lord "diligently" and seeking Him "casually"?

_____

_____

_____

_____

_____

_____

What is one blessing you currently want from your Father in Heaven?

_____

_____

_____

_____

_____

_____

_____

_____

What is your part, or what do you need to do, to help that blessing come to pass?

_____

_____

_____

_____

_____

_____

_____

Chapter Eleven of *Peace Be Unto You* lists a four-step, scripturally based process to help us manage anxiety symptoms. Please review that section before completing the following assignment. This four-step process includes recognizing that something bad has happened, listening to words of truth, acting in faith, and then waiting for the Lord to respond. I'll provide an example from my own life, then you will have the opportunity to examine some examples from your own.

<u>Something bad happens</u>: During his first semester in college, far from home, our son had a grand mal seizure and was rushed to the hospital. As his parents, we sat helplessly as we communicated via text and calls to find out what was happening. My reaction was one of fear and powerlessness.

<u>Listen to words of truth</u>: Despite my fears, I knew the Lord would watch out for our son. I knew he was His son long before he was ours. I had confidence in the doctors and other professionals who would help. However, even despite these truths, I still worried about possible outcomes.

<u>Act in faith</u>: I decided to fast for the welfare of our son. I fasted earnestly and with great desire. I prayed multiple times during my fast, asking for the Lord's intervention and also to help me accept His will.

<u>Wait for the Lord's response</u>: Towards the close of my fast, as I was pondering the situation, I was filled with a feeling of spiritual confidence. I knew for certain that our son would be okay. My faith was strengthened, and I trusted the Lord would resolve the situation.

Now take the opportunity to do the same exercise with an experience from your life. Please choose two separate situations. The first situation needs to be something that has *already happened*. It should be an event where 1) you initially had anxiety about the possible outcome, 2) the outcome has already happened, and 3) things worked out well. The second situation should be something that is *currently happening* where you are worried about the outcome, but the situation has not yet resolved. Respond to the following prompts and questions.

Situation #1 (something that caused you anxiety in the past but *has since resolved*)

Something bad happened: (describe what happened and why it caused you to feel anxiety)

_____

_____

_____

_____

_____

_____

_____

_____

_____

Listen to words of truth: (describe what truths, gospel or otherwise, that helped you feel less anxious)

_____

_____

_____

_____

_____

_____

Act in faith: (describe what you did, what steps you took, to move forward despite your fears)

_____

_____

_____

_____

_____

_____

<u>Wait for the Lord's response:</u> (describe any spiritual feelings you had, or reassurances you received, that the Lord would help manage the situation)

_____

_____

_____

_____

_____

_____

_____

Situation #2 (something that currently causes you anxiety and *has not yet resolved*)

<u>Something bad happens:</u> (describe what happened or is happening and why it causes you to feel anxiety)

_____

_____

_____

_____

_____

_____

Listen to words of truth: (describe what truths, gospel or otherwise, that will help you feel less anxious)

_____

_____

_____

_____

_____

_____

Act in faith: (describe what you can do, what steps you can take, to move forward despite your fears)

_____

_____

_____

_____

_____

_____

<u>Wait for the Lord's response</u>: (describe your faith in how you can receive peace from the Lord, or what things He can do in order to help you manage your current anxious feelings)

_____

_____

_____

_____

_____

_____

_____

Personal confidence is critical to changing our thoughts and actions. If we believe we cannot change, the chances of success are low. Remember that your Father in Heaven is continually watching over you and creating circumstances for your success. He loves you and will do anything for you. The willing sacrifice of His Only Begotten Son should be proof positive of that fact. Please consider the following statement and answer the related questions.

"I can do something about my situation. I can act intentionally. As I combine my efforts with the Savior's power, there is nothing we cannot accomplish together."

To what extent do you agree or disagree with this statement?

_____

_____

_____

_____

_____

_____

_____

To what extent do you want this statement to be true for you?

_____

_____

_____

_____

_____

_____

What personal beliefs do you need to change, if any, to make this statement an accurate description of your current situation?

_____

_____

_____

_____

_____

_____

_____

Please read and ponder these scriptures and answer the following questions.

It is better to trust in the Lord than to put confidence in man (Psalm 118:8).

For the Lord shall be thy confidence, and shall keep thy foot from being taken (Proverbs 3:26).

Therefore, dearly beloved brethren, let us cheerfully do all things that lie in our power; and then may we stand still, with the utmost assurance, to see the salvation of God, and for his arm to be revealed (Doctrine and Covenants 123:17).

What can you do to increase confidence in your own abilities to act in faith and move forward?

_____

_____

_____

_____

_____

_____

What can you do to increase confidence in the fact that the Lord will support and sustain you in your righteous efforts?

_____

_____

_____

_____

_____

_____

_____

Conclusion

Congratulations on the work you've done! Anxiety management can be a very long process, marked by small gains and periodic setbacks. Try to be consistent with the principles you've learned. As you continue to act, you will eventually make progress. Regular, dutiful application of true principles brings us closer to God and refines our natures to become more like Him.

God bless you for your faithful efforts to manage anxiety. If you have diligently tried to apply the principles and applications in this workbook, you may have already noticed a decrease in anxiety symptoms. Even if you haven't noticed such a decrease, you have acted in faith. You've taken the first step. Continue along that path and the Lord will bless you to ultimately have greater peace and less fear.

ABOUT THE AUTHOR

David T. Morgan is a licensed psychologist with more than twenty years of experience in the mental health field. He has a BS in psychology, a MS in counseling and guidance, and a PhD in counseling psychology from Brigham Young University. He and his amazing wife are the parents of six children and two grandchildren. David loves the scriptures and truly believes the answers to life's challenges can be found in the words of ancient and modern prophets. He also loves Disneyland and almost knows more about the Happiest Place on Earth than he does about psychology.

www.ldspsychologist.com

Made in the USA
Las Vegas, NV
21 November 2021

34957503R00080